THE TESLA
DISC TURBINE

by

W.M.J. Cairns
I.Eng., M.I.E.D.

British Library Cataloguing-in Publication-Data: a catalogue record of this book is held by the British Library.

First Printing 2001

ISBN No. 0-9536523-2-7

Published in Great Britain by:

Camden Miniature Steam Services
Barrow Farm, Rode, Frome, Somerset. BA11 6PS

Camden stock one of the widest selections of engineering, technical and transportation book to be found
Write to the above address for a copy of their latest Booklist.

Layout and Design by Camden Studios and Andrew Luckhurst, Trowbridge, Wilts.

Printed and Bound by Salisbury Printing Co. Ltd.

PLEASE NOTE!
In this book the author and publisher are only passing on knowledge; if you decide to build your own Tesla Turbine be aware that your safety, and that of others, is your responsibility, both in the workshop and when running your Turbine. In particular you should appreciate that this machine runs at very high rotational speeds and ALWAYS have a safety guard over it whenever it is run.

FOREWORD

This book describes the concept of the Disc Turbine as originally patented by Nikola Tesla, and provides concept designs for modern versions of the engine, incorporating the Disc Turbine as a power unit for applications in Automobiles and Light Aircraft, and also give descriptions of the original Turbines and the prototype machines.

It also provides designs for other machines operating on the principle of a disc turbine: an Air Compressor, an Air Motor, and a Vacuum Exhauster. The facility of the principle to operate in either a clockwise or anti-clockwise direction of rotation, in a single machine, using only a two-way valve, is described, and applications where this feature can be applied to advantage are suggested.

Data is given on the performances attained by the original engines, together with stress and performance information.

Finally, we give a design for a modernised version of the original turbine, to one half scale, complete with working drawings and manufacturing instructions to enable the model or experimental engineer to construct a fully operational engine, using such tools and equipment as are usually available to model makers.

W.M.J. Cairns,
I.Eng., M.I.E.D. Reg. Engineering Designer
Redditch June 2001

ACKNOWLEDGMENTS

The manufacture and practical development work on the experimental and development Turbines was carried out by G.D. and S. Heeks Engineering, of Storridge, Nr. Malvern, Worcestershire.

Data and information was supplied by Birmingham Reference Library.

Advice on Patents and other Rotary engines was given by Mr. M. Gunn, Patents Manager, Rolls Royce P.L.C.

The author gratefully acknowledges the assistance given by Mr. Adam Harris, of Camden Miniature Steam Services, publisher of this book, in the preparation of the work.

BIBLIOGRAPHY

Prodigal Genius: The Inventions of Nikola Tesla	N. Spearman
So You Think We Should Have a New Engine?	Jet Propulsion Laboratories, California, U.S.A.
The Inventions of Nikola Tesla	George Trinkaus
Report on the Automotive Engine	Economist Research Unit
Some Unusual Engines	L.J.K. Setright, Institute of Mechanical Engineers Publications
Roark's Formulas for Stress and Strain	Roark; McGraw Hill.
Centrifugal Compressors: Flow in Pipes	Atlas-Copco Handbook
The Jet Engine	Rolls Royce Publications
Jet Propulsion	N. Cumsty; Cambridge.

CONTENTS

CHAPTER 1

TESLA'S DISC TURBINE AND COMPRESSOR

The Croatian born inventor and engineer Nikola Tesla is probably best known for his invention of the coil and the induction motor. However, in 1910, a dual patent was filed, under British Patent 24001, for a Rotary Disk type air compressor and turbine engine.

These machines were similar in principle, and comprise a series of thin discs, set close together but separated by spacing washers, mounted on a shaft to form a rotor. This rotor is mounted in a housing, or stator, in the form of a tube, and provided with end plates, which contain the bearings.

The compressor differs from the engine in that the stator takes the form of a spiral volute, whereas that of the engine is circular in profile. The direction of flow of the media, air, or gas also differs.

The patent also identified other applications of the principal, with a motor unit and as a pump for liquids.

The engine formed the principal feature of the patent, and Tesla claimed that creating a very small, but extremely powerful, machine was possible, using the disc principle. Hence it is the engine which formed the first application of the rotary disc which will be considered.

The first experimental machine that was built to prove the principle was a small unit, and consisted of a stack of discs measuring 6 inches diameter, and with a thickness of $1/32$ of an inch, with spacing washers of the same thickness, but of a smaller diameter. These washers were formed in the shape of a cross, with a central hole to match that in the disc. There were eight discs, forming a total width of $1/2$ of an inch.

Following upon the results obtained with this unit, a larger machine was constructed, and gave an output of over 100 horsepower using steam as the medium, whereas the experimental unit utilised compressed air. Larger machines were constructed, one with a rotor of 18 inches diameter, and developing some 200 hp, again using steam as the medium. This weighed 400 lbs. and occupied an area of 2 ft. x 2 ft. x 3 ft. long.

The largest machine to be constructed was of 500 kw. and was made by the *Allis Chalmers Company* of Milwaukee, U.S.A. with whom Tesla had a working agreement. This machine was tested using steam as the medium, and as a single machine, without the use of a condenser or as a multi-rotor combination unit; hence the efficiency was not full exploited, but even so the results were impressive. It was Tesla's intention to incorporate a multi-stage rotor and condenser, this obtaining the maximum thermal efficiency from the system.

While all the machines used steam as the medium, which required steam-raising plant, it was the intention to use liquid fuel to produce the high volumes and pressures in a similar manner to the method used in the present day gas turbines.

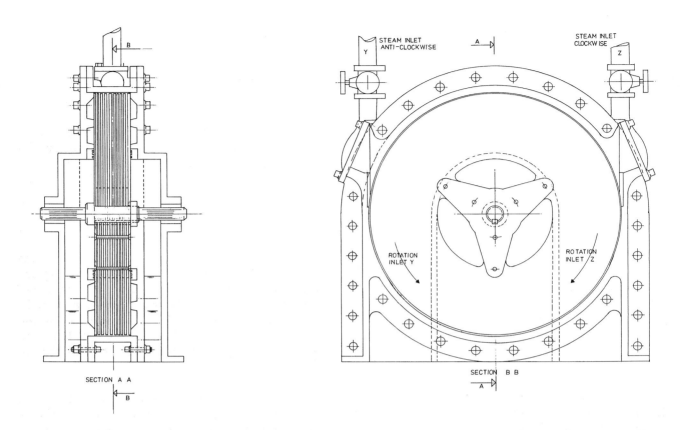

FIG. 1 DISC TURBINE ENGINE BASED ON TESLA'S BRITISH PATENT NO. 24001

The original machines, when examined after testing, were found to have stretched discs due to inertial (centrifugal) forces, and were subject to criticism by the *Allis Chalmers* engineers. The stretching was very likely to be due to the choice of steel for the discs, which probably had a low yield point and resistance to creep. The design of the centre portion of the discs in the area of the porting could also be a contributory factor. It must be borne in mind that at the time the experiments were being carried out, design and metallurgy of materials for use at high temperatures and rotational speeds was limited. Lack of funds prevented further developments of the disc turbine, as the company concentrated its efforts on the manufacture and exploitation of the *Curtis* and *Parsons* type of Impulse and Impulse-Reaction pattern machines, which set the pattern from which subsequent engines, and ultimately the gas turbine, evolved.

It was Tesla's ultimate aim for the engine that a 25 hp. machine could be made to fit inside a bowler hat, and this has now, in fact, been achieved, and even exceeded, by the modern-day small gas turbines for use in model aircraft, where calculated horsepowers of up to 25 hp. and above are being attained, albeit at a low fuel efficiency and life cycle, but with rotational speeds of up to 175,000 revolutions per minute.

After the *Allis Chalmers* machines, the Tesla concept of a rotary disc engine lapsed and no further work was carried out. However, there are some indications that one or two companies are now beginning to take an interest in the principle, and with the availability of the more temperature and creep resistant alloys, and the experience of gas turbine technology, a practical machine becomes a much more feasible proposition, and the Rotary Disc Turbine can provide an alternative power source to the established engine configurations.

CHAPTER 2

DISC TURBINE OPERATING PRINCIPLE

In any prime mover, there are obvious advantages in using a continuous rotary motion, rather than a reciprocating piston/cylinder/crank combination which has high acceleration and decelerations on the components, and requires suitable masses to balance the system, to provide a smooth running machine. Also, to provide a tolerably uniform torque, several cylinders, and a heavy flywheel, are required. Even so, the output is variable, due to the configuration of the engine or other machine.

By adapting a rotary motion, most of these objections are overcome.

The concept of using a stream of flowing medium to obtain a rotary motion is very ancient, and can be seen in the wind and water mills, which were the first prime movers, and continue to this day in the steam and gas turbines and hydraulic turbines and wind powered generating systems. Indeed, the Alexandrian writer Hero, in about 200 B.C., described a reaction turbine which consisted of a sphere of metal, with two tubes at right angles to the periphery. When the sphere was filled with water, and heated over a fire, the reaction from the steam issuing from the tubes cased the device to rotate on the bearings upon which it was mounted. It is even conjectured that the Romans were on the verge of building some form of engine, but the data was lost in the fire that destroyed the library at Alexandria.

The basic reasoning behind the concept of a disc turbine is well understood. When a medium flows through a pipeline, there is a resistance to the flow due to the surface condition of the inner wall, the diameter of the pipe, the rate of flow, and the viscosity of the medium within the pipe. For example, in a long pipeline of relatively small diameter, the resistance to flow will be very high, to such an extent that the pipe would tend to be carried along with the medium were it not constrained to prevent this.

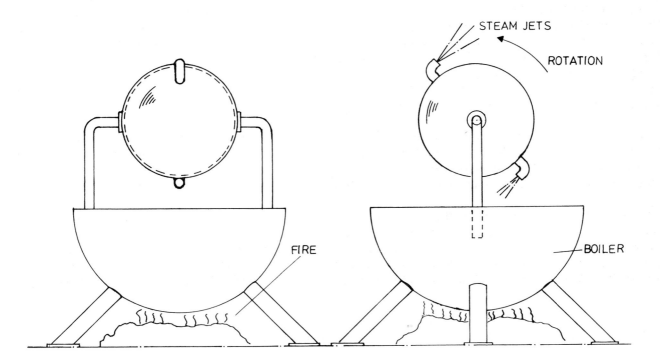

FIG. 2 HERO OF ALEXANDRIA'S STEAM TURBINE

If the pipe is considered in the form of two flat plates, closely spaced together, it can be seen that the plates will move with ever increasing velocity, until the speed matches that of the flowing medium. By replacing the plates with a series of discs, closely spaced and mounted on a shaft, which is in turn supported on bearings, and the disc/shaft combination (the rotor) enclosed within a cylinder (the stator), when a medium is arranged to flow through the spaces between the discs, the rotor will be forced to rotate, at a speed approaching that of the flowing medium. This will be subject to the conditions of the discs, the spacing of the discs, the characteristics of the medium, and the running clearances between the rotor end faces and the rotor/stator diameter clearances.

As the medium flows over the surfaces of the discs, its velocity will decrease as energy is reduced by the work performed, from a maximum at the periphery, and the medium will proceed spirally towards the centre of the discs, where it exhausts to the atmosphere via ports provided in the centre of the discs for this purpose.

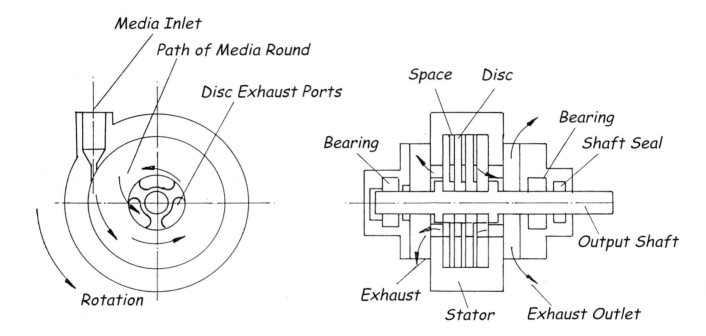

FIG. 3 DIAGRAMATIC ILLUSTRATION OF DISC TURBINE OPERATING PRINCIPLE ENGINE APPLICATIONS

Since the medium, particularly when in gaseous form, such as is obtained by the combustion of fuel as in a gas turbine, will have a very high velocity, then the discs will be caused to rotate at a similar rate, which, with the drag exerted, will result in an engine with a high power output in relation to the size of the machine. The medium may also be in the form of steam, compressed air, or gas (as in a gas turbine) to suit the application and purpose for which the machine is intended.

The basic concept, of a medium flowing over a series of discs, can be applied to other forms of machine where the rotary motion can be used to advantage. For example, to provide a means of compressing air or gas, as a pump for liquids, or as a motor. Some variation in the configuration of the stator will be required, depending on the application of the principle.

Concept drawings of an air compressor, aircraft gas turbine starter motor and air motor, automobile engine, larger engine, and vacuum exhauster are reproduced here, showing the use of the disc principle of operation.

CHAPTER 3

THE FIRST EXPERIMENTAL DISC TURBINE

In the early 1900s the only machines used for power generation and as prime movers were of the reciprocating type, steam driven, and were heavy, essentially still in the form used by the early pioneers of such engines. The motor car and its internal combustion was being developed, and the first aeroplanes were making an appearance.

In 1902, Tesla declared that he was working on a design for an engine that was fundamentally different to the types currently in use, which would be small, simple, and very powerful for its size.

The engine was a turbine, and differed from other such machines which were just being developed by *Parsons* and *Curtis*, later becoming the dominant type.

The first model, for evaluation purposes, was a small machine, weighing about 10 lbs., and measuring, at its largest dimension, no more than 6 inches; on trial it developed around 30 h.p. This exceeded the power-producing capability of every known prime mover in use at the time, returning a power to weight ratio of 3 h.p. for every pound of engine weight.

A description of the operating principle of the concept is given in a separate chapter. This original machine comprised of a stack of discs, as shown in Fig. 4. The material from which these first discs were produced was nickel silver, and of 6 ins. diameter, $1/32''$ thickness, and spaced apart using washers of the same thickness. A stack of eight washers and discs was used, mounted on a shaft of 1 inch diameter, the discs and washers being clamped up to a shoulder by a suitable nut. This assembly formed a rotor, fitted in a cylindrical housing or stator, the ends being closed by plates, which also contained the bearings in which the rotor shaft is located.

In the centre of the discs, and as close to the shaft as practical, ports are formed in the discs, with corresponding gaps in the spacers, to provide an exit for the exhaust of the medium to the atmosphere.

The rotor is a close running fit in the bore, and on the faces of the end plates, to reduce leakage as much as is practicable. Tangentially to the bore of the stator, a nozzle is located through which the medium is directed onto the discs, from whence it flowed in a spiral pattern to the exit ports. For this experimental machine compressed air was used as the operating medium, at a pressure of around 70 p.s.i.

A rotational speed of over 30,000 revolutions per minute was achieved by the machine, and when stripped down for examination, it was found that the discs had stretched by $1/32$ of an inch from the initial diameter. This was due to the inertial loads sustained by the discs at the high rotational speed. The material of the discs, nickel silver, was not ideal for the application, having a relatively low tensile stress value, and elastic yield point. The problem of the elasticity and associated distortion was to manifest itself on later machines, it being a characteristic of the choice of materials available at the time. The problem was aggravated by the design of the disc, which was weakened by the need for the exit ports in the centre.

A drawing of the machine, similar to the experimental unit, is shown in Fig. 4. on the following page This is not an exact copy of the machine as made for Tesla in 1906 by Julius C. Czito, of Astoria, Long Island, in the U.S.A. Tesla evidently made sketches of the machine or components, but only gave a brief explanation to the manufacturer. Thus the drawing shows a machine which is updated to utilise the materials available today, and shows the machine as described by Tesla, who quoted 12 discs, each of 5 ins. diameter, which differs from the description given by the maker, who quotes 8 discs, each 6 ins. in diameter. Therefore the design cannot be said to be a true replica of the original, but can be seen to be a reasonable compromise.

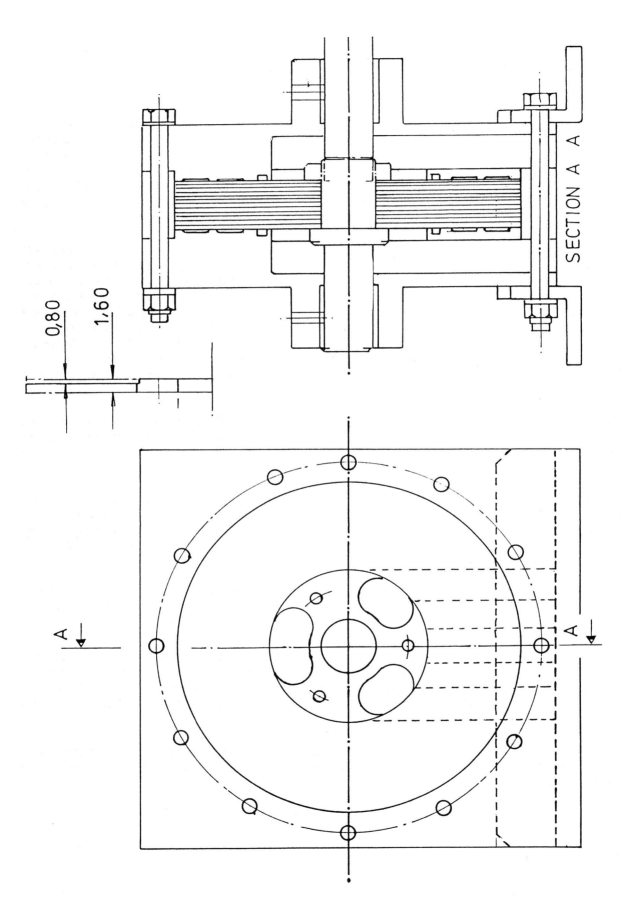

0,80

1,60

SECTION A A

FIG. 4 EXPERIMENTAL DISC TURBINE - 9³/₄" DISCS

CHAPTER 4

THE 9.75 INCH DISC PROTOTYPE TURBINE

Using the experience gained from the small machine, a larger model was designed and manufactured. A drawing of an updated version of a machine of the same proportions as the Tesla model, but making use of present day materials and technology, is shown in Fig. 5. The machine uses a disc of 9 3/4 ins. diameter, and 1/8 inch thick, spaced at 1/32 inch (247.65 and 3.175 mm.). Total width is 52 mm. using thirteen discs. The discs are in stainless steel, and broadly follow the pattern described for the small machine; end covers are in aluminium alloy, as is the stator. The shaft is of carbon steel, running in ball bearings, and a shaft seal is provided, of the conventional rotary seal format.

It is intended that compressed air be used as the medium for this example, and suitable connections and an inlet nozzle are incorporated into the stator. Lubrication is from a reservoir by a drip feed on an absolute loss system, as the machine is not intended as a continuously running unit, but as a development item for a larger scale evaluation of the operating principles. The compressed air is at 80 p.s.i., and the performance is expected to be in excess of 100 h.p. Provision is made in the design to operate the machine using gas generated by a combustion system, but it is only intended to be run for very short periods when operating with this medium. A drawing of this modification is shown in Fig. 5. Air for the combustion system is provided by an external air source, either an independent air compressor, or from a works air network. The air should be free from excess condensate, and from oil contamination. The air connection is shown on the drawing, and should incorporate a shut-off valve, preferably of the ball type.

Fuel is supplied through the union on the adaptor in the stator as shown on the drawing, and delivers the fuel through the needle valve shown. It then mixes with the air from the compressor in the combustor tube, where it is ignited, using the igniter, which is either an electric glow plug or similar device. After the initial combustion, the process becomes self-sustaining.

The heated gas follows the same path as that previously described, namely a spiral circuit round the disc face, and exhausts through the ports as illustrated. The air pressure should be at 50 to 60 p.s.i. (3.4 to 4.0 bar), and the fuel supply, which should be either kerosene or propane, at 100 to 150 p.s.i. (7.0 to 10.0 bar). Propane may be the preferred fuel, as control is simpler, and by using the valve and gauge on the container, the need for fuel pumps and tanks is avoided.

In a research project, it would be useful to provide all three types of medium, i.e. compressed air, gas and steam, in order to evaluate the effects on performance of the different types, and also the effects on the spaces between the discs. It would also serve to cross relate Tesla's results, particularly when using steam.

In all Tesla's machines steam was supplied directly to a single stage, and exhausted to atmosphere. Thus the performance did not take into account the total energy available in the steam, and similarly in the gas powered machine. It was claimed that the 9.75" machine described could provide up to three times the power actually stated, i.e. 330 h.p. Since none of the machines had this feature, it was impossible to verify the figure, but it was certainly the intention to do so.

It was also anticipated that by using gas as the medium, the output from this size machine would increase to 130 to 140 h.p. due to the affinity of the gas to the disc surfaces. Thus, this machine could attain an output of 420 h.p. using a staged rotor.

Multi-stage machines, to an updated configuration, are described in a following chapter.

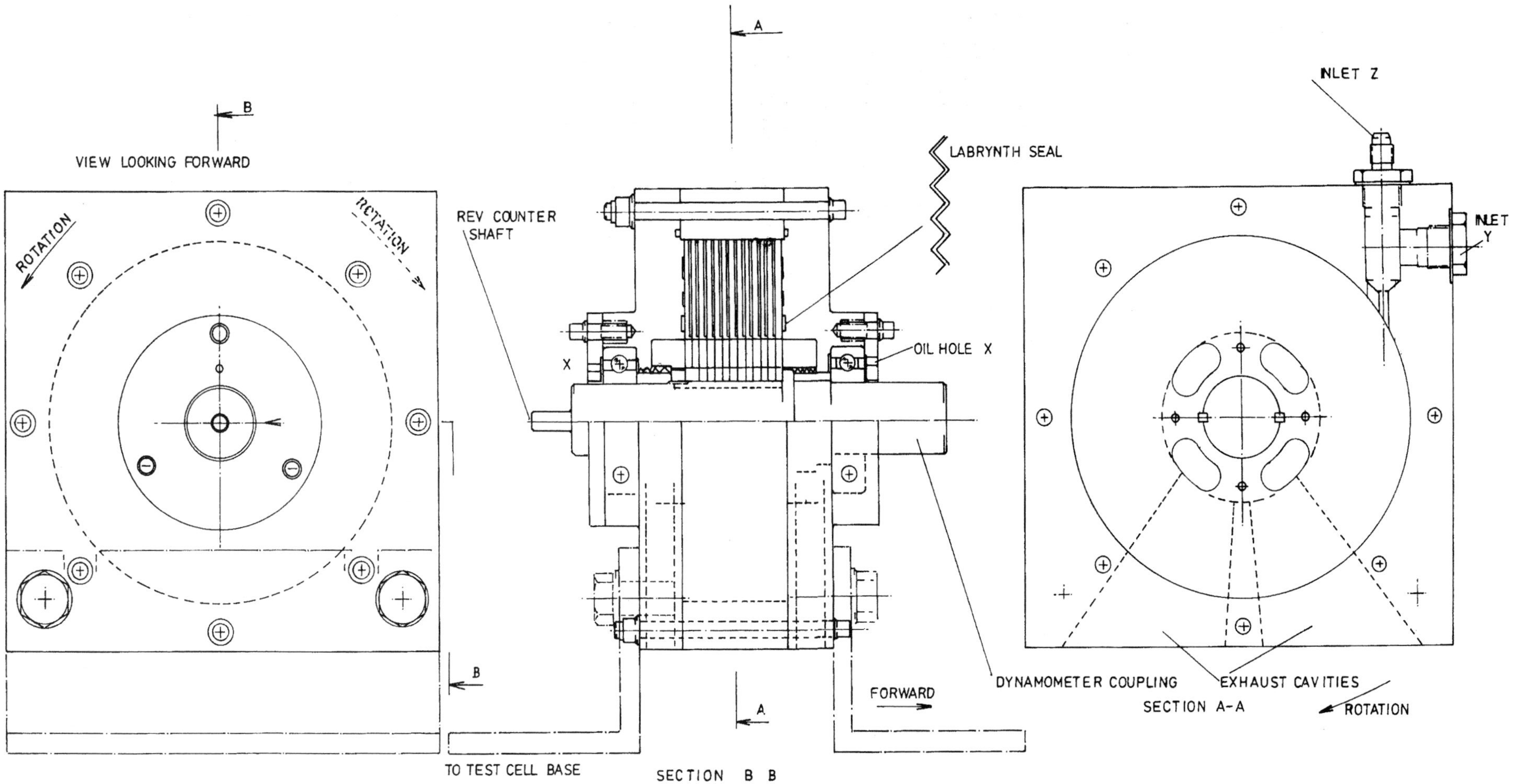

INLET Y

INLET Z

LABRYNTH SEAL

ROTATION

EXHAUST CAVITIES

SECTION A-A

DYNAMOMETER COUPLING

OIL HOLE X

A

A

FORWARD

SECTION B B

IMPORTANT!
This engine must not
be operated without
guards in place

X

REV COUNTER SHAFT

TO TEST CELL BASE

B

B

VIEW LOOKING FORWARD

ROTATION

ROTATION

Tighten fasteners to torque specified
Fit locking inserts to suppliers instructions
Close rivets to detail
Balance rotor assembly to NM static
Oil bearings using Shell "Turbo" or equivalent
Compressed air supply: 100cfm at 60psi
Install pressure gauge at Inlet Y
Install Ball Shut Off valves in fuel and air lines

Compressed air supply at Inlet Z for air powered engine - Inlet Y blanked.
For fuel powered unit, compressed air at Inlet Y and combustion unit fitted
at Inlet Z - fuel inlet at X. Oil supply at oil holes shown.
For fuel powered engine, cooling air is essential.
Maximum continuous running time in fuel mode - 5 minutes

Maximum permitted shaft speed: 9000rpm

FIG. 5 EXPERIMENTAL DISC TURBINE - 5" DISCS

CHAPTER 5

LARGER MACHINES

The next stage in the development of the disc turbine was to produce a larger machine, using a disc of 18 ins. (457.2 mm.)

Two turbines were built, and were tested at the *Edison Company's* Waterside Power station. Each machine developed 200 h.p. was 36" (914mm.) long and 24" (619 mm.) square overall, rotating at 9000 r.p.m. Steam was supplied at 125 p.s.i. and exhausted freely to atmosphere. It was claimed that if the turbine had stages, carrying three rotors in the low pressure unit, with a condenser giving a vacuum of 29" of mercury, such a machine would give an output of 600 h.p., at a very conservative estimate. It was also claimed that the thermal efficiency would approach the theoretical maximum attainable by the Carnot cycle.

The final machine designed by Tesla was the largest unit made using the Disc Turbine concept. It was manufactured by the *Allis Chalmers Manufacturing Company*, and had fifteen discs of 60" (1524 mm.) diameter and 0.125" (3.175 mm.) thickness, spaced 0.125" (3.175 mm.) apart. The design rating was 675 h.p. or 500 Kw. at a speed of 3,600 r.p.m. Steam at 80 p.s.i. was supplied, and a back pressure of 3.0 p.s.i. at the exhaust was noted. It is noted that in the report the steam pressures are quoted as absolute, and may be misinterpreted.

The report by *Allis Chalmers* was critical of the disc turbine, particularly the distortion of the discs by the inertial forces, a force of 70,000 lbs. being quoted. The total costs of the smaller units were deemed uncompetitive with established designs, since it was necessary to provide a reduction gear box to suit pumps or other driven machines. Distortion occurred in the discs, attributed to the light construction, and the opinion was that failure would have resulted in due course. The efficiency was not acceptable, in comparison with established types.

A gas turbine was never constructed, due to lack of the design and technical data to be supplied by Tesla. No further disc turbines were constructed and interest in the principle lapsed.

It should be recognised that much of the criticism, though no doubt correct, failed to take into account the very limited amount of work carried out on the principle, and that only a single stage rotor was used. The company was engaged in development of the impulse and impulse-reaction type machines, as were their competitors, *General Electric* and *Westinghouse*, and they did not wish to compromise their development efforts by proceeding down an uncharted route and risk being left behind in the market-place.

MULTI-STAGE ENGINES

The Disc Turbine engine may be extended to provide greater power outputs, by increasing the diameter and stacks of discs, each stack being of an increasing diameter and number. Thus, as the medium enters the first stack, it is at maximum temperature and pressure, and, as it proceeds from one stage to the next, these characteristics change, as the energy is utilised in the engine.

Generally, the configuration would aim to arrange the major components, i.e. the compressor, combustor, turbine and intermediate sections, on a single shaft, particularly when a constant load and speed engine is required, but for applications where variations in output and operating conditions occur, then a configuration where the compressor is driven by its own dedicated turbine, on its own shaft, and the power turbine is formed by two or more stages mounted on a second shaft, allows better matching of the compressor. The final output may be from an integral gear box, thus making a third shaft configuration.

As an alternative to the integral conformation, the major sections may be arranged as separate units, and connected by suitable pipework or ducting. This form may be particularly advantageous where a separate gas generator is used in place of the compressor and combustor, or when other energy sources, such as waste steam, or exhaust gas, can be usefully recovered.

The range and power outputs possible with the Disc Turbine, using staged rotors, exhausting via a condenser, and using steam as the medium, has never been evaluated, although it was Tesla's declared intention to do so. By employing the modern technique of the closed cycle as used in power stations, where a gas turbine is linked to a steam raising plant to drive a steam turbine, it is highly probable that combining a Disc Turbine driven by gas, either as an integral unit, or from a gas generator, in conjunction with a similar turbine operating on steam raised by a boiler in conjunction with the generator, a high thermal efficiency is possible, and may approach the ideal thermal cycle.

The thermal performance of the Disc Turbine engine may be improved by operating on the Brayton cycle, incorporating a regenerator and associated components in the system, in order to extract the maximum energy from the medium.

The operating principle of the multi-stage turbine is shown diagrammatically in illustration (5), which shows the direction of the flow of the medium from stage to stage through the disc stacks and the intermediate sections, and finally exhausting to the atmosphere.

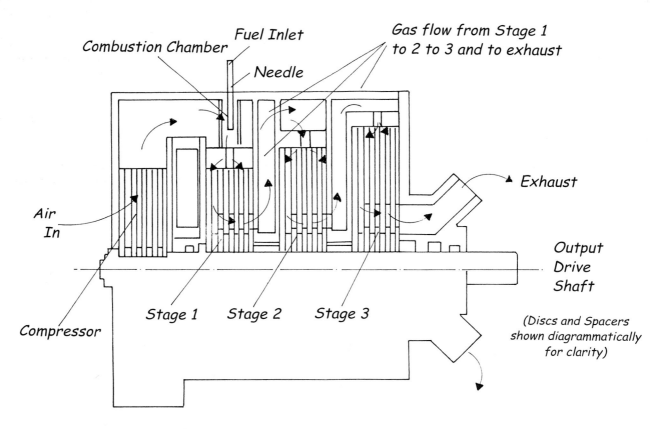

FIG. 6 OPERATING PRINCIPLE OF A THREE STAGE DISC TURBINE WITH THREE POWER ROTORS AND A DISC COMPRESSOR

CHAPTER 6

FUTURE DEVELOPMENTS

Following upon the termination of the work on the large machines carried out by *Allis Chalmers*, development of the Disc Turbine virtually ceased, and no further interest was taken in the principle. All development was concentrated upon the *Parsons* and *Curtis* impulse-reaction and impulse turbines, for the electrical power generation industries and marine applications, and the rapidly growing reciprocating internal combustion engine for automotive and aircraft usage.

The development of the gas turbine in the 1940s led to its application for aero use on all but the smallest aircraft, and, latterly, this engine form has found increasing use in combined power generation systems, where it has very high thermal efficiencies.

The only other engine form that has been developed as a viable alternative to the I/C and turbine engines has been the Wankel, but in comparison with the other two major engine types, the numbers have been very small.

In a survey carried out by the *Jet Propulsion Laboratories* of California, it was identified that the engines which were the most likely candidates for future developments using fossil fuels were those operating on the *Stirling* or *Brayton* cycle. The Tesla Disc Turbine was omitted from the survey,which was a major oversight in what was ostensibly an in-depth survey of future engine development.

A further report by *The Economist* research unit identified that fossil fuels are likely to be the main energy source, pending development of alternative sources, such as fuel cells or batteries.

A limited amount of development work was undertaken by Tesla on the use of a heated gas, as in a gas turbine, as the medium, and he claimed that this would give a superior performance to that obtained by the use of steam but the details of the proposal were not forthcoming.

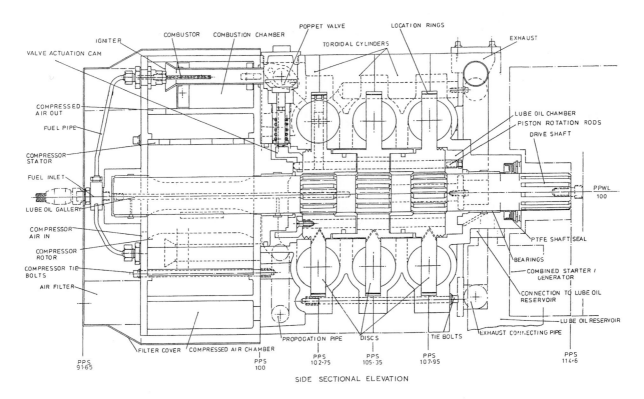

FIG. 7 AN ALTERNATIVE ROTARY ENGINE CONFIGURATION

The Rotary disc concept has been sadly neglected for over 60 years, as engine makers concentrated their research and development on the established turbine and reciprocating designs.

Tesla's personality has been quoted as a major factor in the lack of interest in the concept, and for further details of the turbine and other inventions, and a personal biography of this most talented engineer, the reader is referred to the book "Prodigal Genius" by N. Spearman.

It may well be that the time is now opportune to take a long, hard look at the concept of a Rotary Disc Turbine Engine, based upon the principles propounded by Tesla, and designed to incorporate the advances made in materials and manufacturing technology, drawing upon the expertise gained in the development of the gas and steam turbines and internal combustion engines, to exploit the advantages and properties inherent in this unique, and far too long neglected, form of engine, and its related machines, such as compressors, air motors and others.

CHAPTER 7

OTHER ROTARY ENGINES

There are but two established forms of rotary engine, the turbine, using gas, steam or water, either as an impulse, or impulse-reaction format, and the Wankel type, using a profiled rotor.

Despite the advantages of a smooth and constant torque, low vibration levels, and the absence of valves, and with a high power to weight ratio, and relatively simple configuration, the rotary engine has not made any great inroads into the automotive and transportation industry, except in aircraft, where the gas turbine is supreme, and in a few trains and trucks. *General Motors* and the former *Rover* company had gas turbine powered vehicles, as evaluation units only, and no volume production was ever introduced.

There have been many patents for rotary engines, some quite bizarre, but few could be considered as being a practical proposition. As far as is known, none ever reached the manufacturing stage, and very few were actually built, even as experimental units. One form of such an engines is shown in Fig. 7.

Probably the most successful alternative to the I/C engine was the Stirling Cycle machine, developed as a joint venture by the *Phillips Electrical Co.*, and the *Ford Motor Co*. This was not a true rotary machine, but employed a swash plate format, but did not progress beyond the experimental stage. This swash plate, or 'wobble plate', configuration was used in several engines, notably by the *Bristol Aeroplane Company*, and a twelve cylinder steam powered machine, using the same principle, was constructed by the late Mr. Hutchison, the model engineer. As we remarked in a previous chapter, with the use of fossil fuels likely to continue for some time, it is appropriate to consider the Disc Turbine as a power source.

While the disc principle can be utilised for other applications, it is as an engine that it has the most potential. The format is suitable for most of the applications normally met by the internal combustion engine, of any configuration, and may have applications for light aircraft.

It is as a power unit for the automobile that the Disc Turbine has the most potential. This is the only industry that has the resources to develop the concept, and which has the most to gain from the unique features of the machine.

Using the disc turbine principle provides an engine that has a high power to weight ratio, simple configuration, low grade fuel requirements, high thermal efficiency, and low unit costs, as well as significant reductions in emissions and noise levels.

A major investigation is being undertaken by a group of five European automobile manufacturers, *Volvo*, *Volkswagen*, *Daimler-Benz*, *BMW*, and *PSA*, which co-ordinates the programme. Two firms specialising in gas turbines, *Garret* and *Onera*, are also taking part, with *Le Moteur Moderne* developing a rotary heat exchanger, and *Rhone-Poulenc* providing data on ceramics and composite materials. Work is also in hand on the combustion chamber, bearings and reduction gearing.

A complete definition of the final machine is not presently available, but from the information released the engine will be of 100 Kw. power, two shaft construction, with a centrifugal compressor, gas generator turbine, axial single stage power turbine, variable turbine entry deflectors, and a rotating regenerator. The engine will operate on the Brayton cycle, details of which are available in the *Jet Propulsion Laboratory* book, or any textbook on heat engines or gas turbines.

As stated in a previous chapter on a similar project, the Disc Turbine is not currently featured in this investigation but could no doubt compete successfully with the conventional unit being proposed, both in performance, efficiency and other features, and may well have the edge in price and manufacturing capability.

A projected design for a Disc Turbine engine, of a similar power output, together with a suggested concept for a vehicle system, is the subject of the following chapter.

CHAPTER 8

AUTOMOTIVE DISC TURBINE

The most important application for the Disc Turbine is as a power unit for automobiles. Such an engine, suited to the average passenger car, could be a three-shaft unit, and comprising of an integral compressor, combustor, power turbine, and a reduction gearbox.

Such an engine is illustrated in Fig. 8. The engine as shown occupies an envelope of 305 mm. cube, and has an estimated weight of 30 kgs., with a power output of 75 horsepower at the drive shaft, and an overall output of 85/90 horsepower. In the design a centrifugal type compressor is used, this being a well established format, but a disc type could be configured. It is mounted on an independent shaft with its dedicated turbine unit, thus allowing optimum matching of this item to the air requirement.

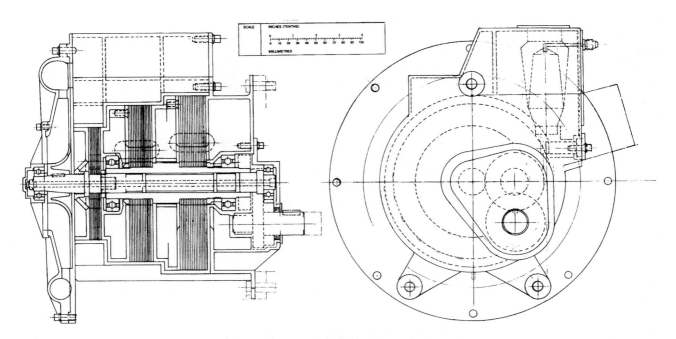

FIG. 8 AUTOMOTIVE DISC TURBINE ENGINE

The power turbine comprises two disc stacks mounted on a common shaft, and of two different diameters, to accommodate the difference in the energy content of the medium as it passes from one stage to the next, via the intermediate section.

The stators for the rotors form part of the housings which contain the bearings, and galleries for the passage of the medium from the combustor to rotor stacks and intermediate sections. The combustor is also located in the said housings, and is comprised basically of two tubes, with a needle located in the centre. Air is directed from the compressor to the outer tube, thence by way of a suitable passage to the inner tube, where it mixes with the fuel, supplied via a tube from the fuel tank. The fuel and air is so proportioned as to ensure stoichiometric combustion; the remaining air flows over the flame tube and is admitted to the tube at various points, and finally the hot, diluted gases flow into the stator via a slot in its wall, and hence into the disc spaces. The manner in which the gas proceeds through the turbine has been described in previous chapters.

Control of the fuel into the combustor is by a simplified form of the FADEC system employed on aircraft gas turbines, this unit also monitoring temperature, shaft speed, fuel consumption, electrics and gas values. Temperatures and pressures will be low in comparison with aircraft turbines, being in the order of 8 bar and 1000°C.

Estimates of fuel requirements are difficult to predict, being dependent on many variables, but for average cruise motoring, 80 miles to a gallon, using kerosene, is reasonable, and may be conservative. Manufacturing and material costs of the engine are very obviously dependent on volume and facilities available, and the materials selected for the components, but it is highly probable that they will be one half that of an equivalent conventional engine. Fuel costs will also be much lower, assuming kerosene at present levels, but it is, of course, not certain that this will remain the case.

Maintenance is extremely simple, being limited to washing out the discs using hot water and detergent, and infrequent oil changes. The most likely component to wear is the combustor, for which a life of 7,500 hours is the target, but its lifespan may be much greater, according to the materials used. No major wear is expected on other items, and life-span of 20,000 hrs. is a distinct possibility.

A Disc Turbine Vehicle Concept

The Disc Turbine engine offers an opportunity to capitalise on some of the unique features of the machine.

Apart from the smooth running of the turbine due to the rotary motion, the compact size and low weight allow greater freedom to the body designer, and the *incorporation of the gearbox* into the configuration gives further scope for the installation. The running characteristics allow the use of hydraulic or electric transmissions, thus avoiding the clutch and **gearbox units**, and the availability of air from the compressor allows the use of power braking systems, power steering, ride control, in-car heating or air conditioning, and de-misting, without any extra units being required.

Wind-screen wipers using an air jet are another prospect, as is door locking, horn operation, headlamp dipping, and, obviously, tyre inflation.

An electric drive, using a light-weight generator of the type being developed by *Turbo-Genset*, from research carried out by *Imperial College*, offers many advantages, not the least being an instant drive-away facility, and a limited no-fuel range, assuming a suitable battery facility is provided.

One further possibility of employing the versatility of the Turbine is to use it as an air motor, and equip the vehicle with a series of high pressure air reservoirs, thus running the vehicle on compressed air, with no pollution whatsoever. Such a proposal, using a reciprocating unit, is under active consideration in France and Mexico.

A useful range and speed can be obtained from reservoirs charged to 40 bar, and the vehicle is extremely simple, with no gearbox, fuel tank or engine, and can be of very light construction.

CHAPTER 9

AIR COMPRESSOR, VACUUM PUMP, AIR MOTOR, LIGHT AIRCRAFT ENGINE

DISC COMPRESSOR

The Disc Compressor is similar in layout to the turbine, with a rotor made up of a stack of discs, spaced apart, mounted upon a shaft, and running in a housing or stator. The pressures generated by the unit are dependent upon the speed of rotation and the number of stacks of discs, or stages. A single stage machine will deliver air at up to 6 bar, at a shaft speed of 15,000 to 20,000 r.p.m. in volumes up to 100 cubic feet per minute free air, the air being virtually free from oil. The size of the unit is much less than a conventional vane, screw or reciprocating machine, with minimal vibration and noise levels.

Configuration of the Disc Compressor is the same as the turbine, and is shown diagrammatically in Fig. 10, the major difference being the profile of the bore of the stator, which is in the form of a spiral volute, and the absence of the inlet nozzle. The discs are also different in that the ports in the centre, near the shaft, have a spiral form, to aid the air flow.

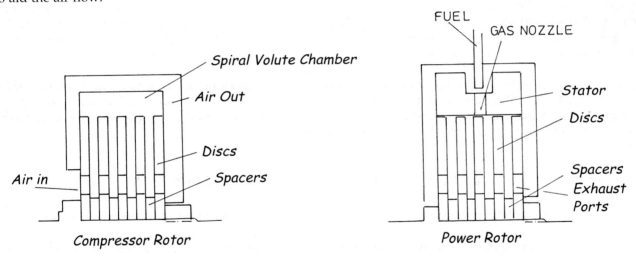

FIG. 9 DIAGRAMMATIC VIEWS OF COMPRESSOR AND POWER DISC AND STATOR UNITS

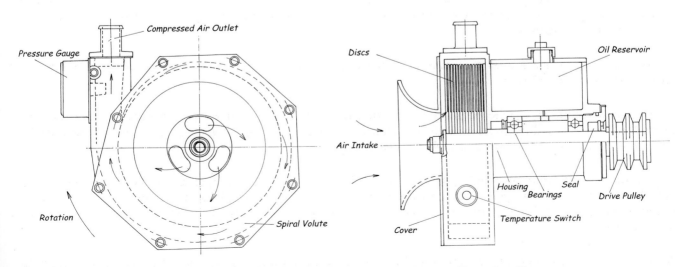

FIG. 10 END AND SIDE ELEVATIONS OF A SINGLE STAGE ROTARY DISC AIR COMPRESSOR

In operation, the shaft is rotated by a suitable prime mover, causing the rotor to turn, drawing in air from the atmosphere into the centre of the discs, from where it is directed via the shaped ports into the spaces between the discs. It is thence flung outwards to the periphery of the discs by the centrifugal force so generated, into the spiral volute in the stator, the velocity of the air changing from kinetic to pressure energy as it decelerates.

The air may progress round the spiral or entrain at an intermediate point, dependent upon the point of entry relative to the volute throat. Cooling of the machine is by a suitable fan, which is incorporated in the drive, but with the thin sections used in the components, much of the heat of compression is expected to be dissipated by radiation. Lubrication is required only to the bearings, being supplied by a dead loss drip feed from a small reservoir. Controls on the machine are a pressure switch and gauge, and an over-temperature device.

Materials are aluminium alloy for the stator and housings, steel for the shaft, with the discs of alloy, stainless steel or titanium, the choice being determined by the duty and size of the unit.

Maintenance is simple, being only to maintain the oil level in the reservoir, and occasionally wash out the discs and housings with detergent and hot water, there being no need to dismantle the machine, and with no rubbing surfaces, wear will be limited to the erosion effects at the throat, which is limited to a very small amount by reinforcement.

The compressor forms part of the original British Patent Number 24001, taken out by Tesla, the design shown being a modernised and updated version of this, with improvements to details and materials.

DISC TURBINE VACUUM EXHAUSTER

Conventional vacuum exhausters may be of either the positive displacement or dynamic type, for most general applications where around 28" to 30" depression is required. The Disc Turbine Vacuum Exhauster complements these types, and has the advantage of being smaller, with no sliding vanes, pistons and cranks, and it is also oil free. It develops a higher level of vacuum than the fan or centrifugal types, and is much more robust and simpler to maintain in service.

The Disc Turbine Exhauster comprises of a series of thin discs, closely spaced, and mounted on a shaft to form a rotor. This rotor is supported in bearings, which are located in a housing, with a spiral volute formed therein. The discs have a series of ports arranged close to the surface of the shaft, and align with an intake flare, which is connected to the vacuum chamber or reservoir. The exhauster illustrated in Fig. 11 is constructed integrally with the motor frame, and mounts on a common shaft, but may be an independent unit, with a belt or other suitable drive system.

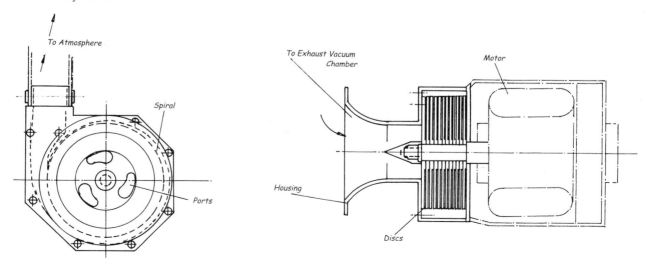

FIG.11 END AND SIDE ELEVATIONS OF A DISC TURBINE VACUUM EXHAUSTER

In operation, the vacuum is generated in the chamber or equipment it is desired to evacuate, via a connection on the intake flare. The air or gas is drawn through the intake and proceeds in a spiral pattern round the discs, and into the volute, from where it exits through the outlet to atmosphere.

AIR STARTER MOTOR

The conventional gas turbine air starter motor is usually of the vane type, and is a well proven design. As with all vane motors, the air pressure is applied to the vane to provide the torque at a small radius, relative to the diameter, rather than at the periphery, due to the disposition of the vane in the stator. By using the disc turbine motor, the torque can be applied in a more advantageous manner, by a tangential approach to the rotor.

The turbine disc Air Starter Motor comprises of a series of discs, mounted on a shaft, and closely spaced, separated by spacing washers, or a shoulder formed integrally with the disc, to form a rotor. This rotor is located in a stator, the ends of this stator being closed by housings which contain the bearings, and also provide the exhaust porting for the exhaust air. An inlet for the air supply in incorporated in the stator, and a nozzle also in the stator directs the air onto the discs.

In operation, compressed air is admitted through the inlet, and directed onto the discs at a tangent to the periphery, and flows in a spiral pattern round the discs, exhausting through the ports provided in the discs, close to the shaft surface. The manner in which the disc turbine functions is described in detail in an earlier chapter.

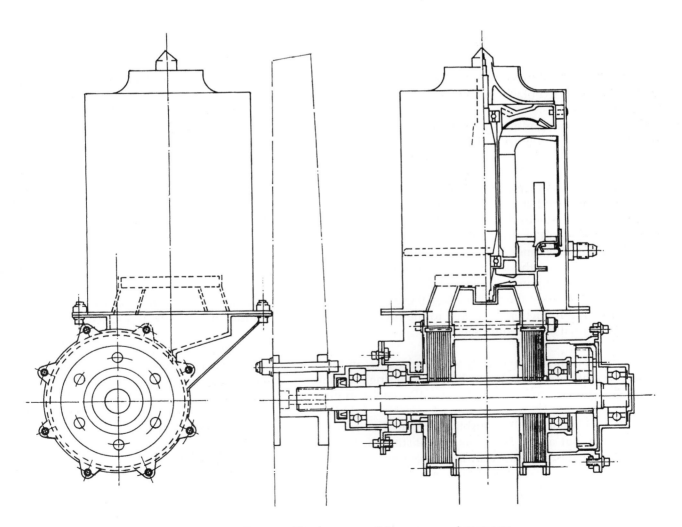

FIG. 12 DISC TURBINE ENGINE FOR A MICROLIGHT AIRCRAFT

As with all air motors, where a high power output is required, for example in a gas turbine starter, a high volume of air is required, usually for a short period. It is anticipated that the disc turbine motor will provide a greater output, for the same volume of air, than the vane for the same volume of air, due to the greater efficiency derived from the manner in which the air is utilised, and the better torque applied due to the configuration of the disc and input nozzle.

Materials for the motor described are suited to aero-space applications, with the discs being in titanium, shaft in stainless steel, and housings and stator in wrought aluminium alloys. However, for less weight conscious applications, for general industrial use, less expensive materials are substituted, with stainless steel discs and carbon steel for the shaft, and cast aluminium housings and stator. Since in such applications the operating mode will be continuous, the lubricating system and cooling will be modified to suit such conditions.

The motor is simple to maintain, requiring only washing out occasionally with detergent and hot water, and the lubrication of the bearings. There are no vanes or rubbing or sliding faces to deteriorate, the only running faces being the bearings and seals. This motor is also tolerant of contamination by debris and water in service.

LIGHT AIRCRAFT DISC TURBINES

The application of the Disc Turbine engine concept to power an aircraft is possibly the most challenging. It is likely that the best option is a power plant for a small light aircraft, or micro-light, machine, using a configuration similar to that adapted for the car engine, but of the lightest possible construction, and using more sophisticated materials for the critical components. For a large engine such as would be required as an alternative to a present-day gas turbine, a different form of construction would be necessary, since the solid disc, as previously noted, has limitations on the diameter that can be accommodated, and must be able to resist the inertial forces imposed upon it. A disc diameter of ten to twelve inches would seem to be the upper limit of diameter that can be comfortably accommodated, with reasonable stress values and the highest practical speeds, and still give an acceptable power:weight ratio.

Two proposed designs are shown in Fig. 12 and Fig. 13, one form being a power unit for a micro-light aircraft, of a nominal 10 h.p. output, the other being intended for a larger machine, having an output of 70 h.p. This engine would also suit an automobile or motor cycle application, where weight is important.

A conventional gas turbine configuration is adopted for both engines, with a compressor, combustion section, and first and second stage disc turbine power sections. There are, however, major differences to the simpler format used on engines described earlier. To obtain optimum performances from the compressor and turbine sections, a two-shaft or three-shaft configuration is used, with separate shafts for the compressor, turbines and power output functions. Also, the combustion section is a separate section, and uses an annular form, with burners, rather than the simpler integral form. A centrifugal type compressor, driven by its own dedicated turbine, can be configured, in place of the disc type. This feature allows the compressor to run at a much higher speed, independent of the power discs, these being mounted on a second dedicated shaft, which drives a third shaft through a reduction gear box, to the final output shaft, which may now rotate at a speed suited to the propeller or final drive requirements.

The gear box is formed integrally with the engine, and may be offset, or in line, as suited to the installation. To reduce weight the stators are combined into a single section, with diameters suited to the first and second stages, and utilise a spacer in between the two disc stacks, in place of the separate unit.

For the small machine the turbine driving the compressor is a single stage reaction type, of one piece construction, but a disc stack can be substituted, this requiring additional space, and adding extra weight. Moreover, the design of the centrifugal compressor, and its turbine and combustor, is to an established format, which can reduce development time in introducing a prototype engine.

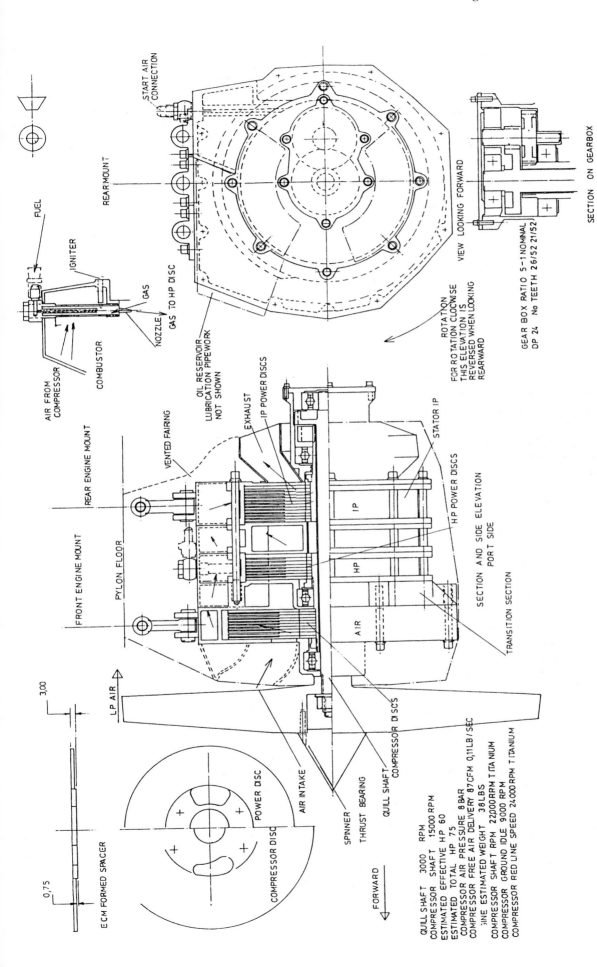

FIG. 13 TWO STAGE DISC TURBINE ENGINE FOR LIGHT AIRCRAFT APPLICATION, WITH INTEGRAL GEAR BOX

CHAPTER 10

DUAL DIRECTION FACILITY

A unique feature of the Tesla Disc Turbine is the ability to operate in either a clockwise or anti-clockwise direction of rotation by changing the position of the inlet ports for the medium, relative to the centre line. This is readily accomplished by providing two input ports, at opposed positions of 180° to each other in the stator or stators.

Thus, by installing a two-way valve in the supply line to the turbine, the direction may be changed from one to the other simply by operating the valve. This is particularly useful for an air motor installation when either clockwise or anticlockwise rotation is required, and avoids the need for any form of reversing equipment.

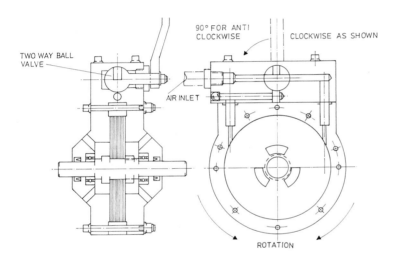

**FIG. 14 DISC TURBINE AIR MOTOR WITH
DUAL DIRECTION FACILITY**

The feature may be incorporated in an engine where the direction is required to be reversed; for example, in an automobile application the reversing gear in the gearbox is not required, and reverse may be selected by the use of a two-way valve. To incorporate this feature, the configuration of the engine will differ from that shown in Chapter 8, in that the gas from the combustor would be directed to the nozzle through the two-way valve, instead of directly onto the discs, as shown. Obviously the engine would have to be stopped, to allow for the change, and this may require a brake to enable the change to be made quickly, although the incoming gas will oppose the direction of rotation, and cause the change to be implemented.

When the operating medium is steam or compressed air, the direction of the flow through the two-way valve will present no difficulties; these may, however, occur with the higher temperatures experienced using gas generated in the combustor, and which will therefore require high temperature resistant alloys to be used for the valve. In automobile applications, the use of a gearbox reverse may be preferred, but in applications where a rapid reverse is not necessary, such as in a truck or tractor/trailer, no great difficulties should arise.

There is an application for a disc turbine where the facility to be able to operate in either direction of rotation, by means of a simple valve, has a distinct advantage, this being where it is employed as a power unit in a steam locomotive. Steam turbines have been used for locomotives, the best known being the Pacific designed by Stanier for the former L.M.S., the "Turbomotive". This had two turbines, a small one for reverse, and a larger one for forward running; these could have been replaced by a single disc unit, with a two-way valve.

Another application, and one that offers the best opportunity to exploit this feature, is the compressed air-driven vehicle, being developed for use in France and Mexico. In this case, the turbine would incorporate an integral reduction gear unit in the design, and avoid the need for any reverse function, making a very simple installation possible.

CHAPTER 11

STRESSES IN COMPONENTS

The principal stress in the Disc Turbine is the inertial stress in the disc, caused by the speed of rotation. This stress is a function of the centrifugal force generated in any rotating body, and may be computed from the well known equation for such a condition. For an indication of the stress levels in the disc the equations from Roark's manual may be quoted.

Consider the disc as a rotating item with a central hole; then, for the tangential stress:-

$$ft \;=\; \frac{qw^2}{4\,G} \left[\, (\,3+v\,)\,r^2 + (\,1-v\,)\,ro^2 \,\right]$$

and for the radial stress:-

$$fr \;=\; \frac{3+m}{8\,G} \;\times\; qw^2\,(\,r-ro\,)^2$$

where:

q = weight per unit volume
w = angular velocity in radians/second
v = Poissons Ratio

r = radius of outer diameter
ro = radius of central hole
G = gravitational constant = 386.4

All dimensions are in inches, loads in pounds

DISC GAS TURBINE PERFORMANCE

The power output and performance of the disc turbine is influenced by the condition of the surfaces of the discs, the spacings, gas temperature, velocity and pressure, and the internal restrictions and constraints. Stress levels in the discs also are a restraint on the configuration when using solid disc formats.

Some indication of the performance which can be expected can be obtained by extrapolation of results from data supplied by original test figures, suitably amended, and from simplified calculations and assumptions based upon the flow of gas through tubes. The basic gas laws obviously apply to the compressor and turbine gas pressure, volume, and temperature conditions.

PERFORMANCE BY EXTRAPOLATION

From quoted values for a disc turbine of 9.75 " diameter, and running at around 9000 r.p.m. a performance of 110 h.p. was returned, using steam at 125 p.s.i.

$$\text{Then:-} \quad 110 = 9000 \times F \times 3.14 \times 0.60 / 3300$$

This gives a value for F of 214

Using this value the performance for a machine with a 7" disc approximates to:

$$\text{H.P.} = 9000 \times 214 \times 3.14 \times 0.58 / 33000 = 106$$

This is a very crude approximation, and takes no account of the undoubted variations due to differing conditions between the two machines.

STRESS IN DISCS

The major considerations in the design of the disc turbine are the inertial stresses in the discs, at the rotational speed required.

Stress levels are limited to those which can safely be accommodated within the yield point and temperature/creep conditions which will occur, using, where practical, stainless steel alloys, or, when necessary, heat resistant materials such as *Inconel* or *Nimonic* alloys. For the seven inch diameter discs used in the machine for automotive applications the stress levels are as follows:-

Using the form identified in *Roark*, Chapter 15, for a solid disc with a central hole, then for radial stress:-

$$Fr = \frac{3 + v}{8} \times \frac{qw^2}{G} \times (R - Ro)^2$$

where:

v = Poisson Ratio = 0.3
q = Density = 0.28 lbs./cu. in.
w = Angular velocity in Radians/Sec

R = Radius at outer rim in inches = 3.5 ins.
Ro = Radius of hole on centre in inches = 0.7 ins.
All dimensions are in inches, loads in pounds

Substituting values in above, then at 9000 rpm:

$$Fr = 0.4125 \times 643 \times 7.84 = 2079 \text{ lbs./sq. inch.}$$

Then for tangential stress:

$$Ft = \frac{1}{4} \frac{qw^2}{G} (3 + v)R^2 + (1 - v)Ro^2$$

Substituting values in the above, then at 9000 rpm:

$$Ft = \frac{643}{4} \times (40.425 + 0.34)$$

$$= \frac{643}{4} \times 40.76$$

$$= 6552.17 \text{ lbs./sq.in.}$$

For maximum permitted "Red Line Speed" at 15000 rpm
At 18200 lbs./sq.inch yield, maximum rpm = 15000

BURSTING SPEED STRESS

The average stress on a diametral plane gives a better criterion for safety margins than that computed from formulae for elastic conditions, since cases are known where failure at 61% of U.T.S. has occurred.

From case 8 of *Roark*, bursting stress for a disc is as previous examples.

$$Fa = \frac{qw^2 \ (R^3 - Ro^3)}{3G \ (R - Ro)}$$

Substituting values in the above, this gives a stress value at 9000 R.P.M. of 3662.4 lbs./sq.inch.

This is well within the elastic limit for the materials proposed, and including the softening and creep conditions likely to be experienced under normal use.

Performance based upon flow through tube. Let:-

w   = flow velocity in metres/second
L   = Pipe length in metres
f   is a factor, value of 0.04
D   is the diameter of tube equivalent in metres
P   is the fluid density in Kgs. per cubic metre at 1.225

then from *Centifugal Compressors: Flow in Pipes* (Atlas-Copco handbook):- Resistance $= f \times {}^1\!/_D \times {}^{PW}\!/_2 \times 10$

Equivalent tube size for a gap between plates of 0.025" based on 10 revolutions at 0.25" centres, gives a total tube length of 130.4" or 3.312 metres.

Substituting these values in the above gives a pressure of 2.554 bar.

Then horsepower for each disc:- H.P. = F x A x L x R.P.S./550

Let:-

F   =   Total pressure on disc in pounds
A   =   Mean effective diameter of disc, in feet, 0.375
L   =   3.14

This evaluates to a horsepower/disc at 11.6 and allowing an efficiency of 75% gives 8.75 horsepower.

Then, with 12 effective discs, total turbine horsepower is 12 x 8.75 = 105 horse-power for the machine.

CHAPTER 12

A MODEL DISC TURBINE

The model described is approximately one half the size of the original Tesla unit, but uses present-day materials and techniques, and is devised so as to be made by the average model engineer, using tools and equipment generally available. Some metal-working experience is assumed, and a basic understanding of drawings. Required machine tools are a lathe, with a 3.5" centre height, ideally with a milling attachment, and circular table, a bench drill, micrometer or vernier, and conventional hand tools.

While the drawings define specific dimensions and tolerances, these can be amended to suit the tools available; for example, the threads may be to B.A. or U.N.F. and the toleranced dimensions adjusted, providing that the specified relative clearances are maintained. An air pressure source is required to drive the turbine, capable of supplying 2 bar and 1.5 cu. ft. per minute free air. A propellant may be adapted as an alternative, or a model stationary steam engine boiler could possibly be utilised.

Materials required are:-

– aluminium bar, 85 mm. diameter;
– steel bar 12 mm. diameter;
– aluminium sheet, ideally Duralumin, hard temper, of 1.25 mm. thickness
– and 270 mm. x 360 mm. cut into 90 mm. squares;
– a small piece of bronze, 12 mm. diameter;
– a 50 mm.length of 100mm. diameter tube;
– a small piece of steel or brass plate 4 mm. thick.

Some materials may also be needed for jigs and templates, such as:-

– a square piece of aluminium 80 mm. x 80 mm., and 12 mm. thick;
– a piece of silver steel;
– a piece of steel plate 1.5 mm. thick for a template.

These latter items are at the discretion of the model maker, to suit his method of making the discs.

Stock items required are:-

– 9 off M4 x 35 bolts;
– 2 off M3 x 10 screws;
– an M8 stiffnut;
– 9 off M4 hexagon stiffnuts;
– 3 off aluminium rivets, with countersunk heads and 15mm. long;
– Loctite **Studlock**;
– a piece of 0.075 mm. thick Mylar film, 180 mm. x 180 mm., for the gaskets, as required.

MAKING THE PARTS

The methods described are intended as a guide, and are similar to those used to make the prototype. Individuals may prefer to use different methods, to suit their own particular skills, and the equipment available.

The stator and end covers, *items 1, 2 and 3,* are turned from aluminium bar, boring and facing the ends, maintaining the concentricities and squareness as shown. The bearing bush, *item 6,* can be fitted to the end covers while in the lathe; note that the bush has a lead-in chamber. Use a suitable peg to align squarely, and finish, ream or bore to size.

The stator has a slot which cuts through the bore. This is cut with an end mill, and may be sized as shown, or left with material on, if experimentation with inlet sizes is required. As the part is cut through, it may be advisable to make a support ring to prevent spring-back, taking care when sizing to use only a light cut due to the presence of the slot.

Finally, drill the flange fixing holes, and tap the inlet adaptor holes.

The shaft, *item 5*, is a conventional lathe turning task; note that a trimming allowance is left on, as shown. Cut the keyway using a 2 mm. dia. end mill, keeping central, and in line with the shaft axis.

FIG. 15 COMPLETE MODEL DISC TURBINE ENGINE

Bearing surfaces are polished. Concentricity of the identified dimensions is important, and if possible, these features should be ground.

The ten discs, *item 4*, are probably the most difficult part to make. Ideally, they would be produced by electro-chemical machining, but this requires specialised equipment which is not readily available to model engineers.

The method described is the process by which the prototypes were made, and is based on the practice used to make P.C. boards. It requires a milling head, and a rotary table, but the item can be made by careful drilling and filing.

Hard aluminium is the material used, cut into 90 mm. squares, and a template will be required, as will a template for the spacing portion, and a suitable location peg. More experienced modellers may not need the template. The disc blanks are attached to a similar sized piece of alloy, using suitable screws.

The unit is mounted onto a rotary table, and using a 6 mm. diameter end mill, the profile of the spacer and the ports are milled out, with holes drilled for the rivets, as shown. Use a sharp, preferably new, cutter, with fine feed and high speed. Cut the key slot, filing carefully, or slot on the miller. The disc is now rotated, using the same cutter, and the outer diameter cut, leaving four equally spaced nibs to retain the disc in the sheet, with an allowance left on the outer diameter for final finishing to size, as an assembly.

The discs may be cut by hand, with the spacer formed separately, leaving a finishing allowance on the outer diameter. The milling head may be traversed axially and longitudinally, thus not requiring a rotary table, the final shapes being made by hand finishing. When completed, the disc can be removed from the support and the nibs cut off. Finally, trim the disc to remove all burr, noting the remarks regarding square edges.

The two bearing bushes, *item 6*, are turned from a suitable material; bronze is specified as this is probably the easiest to obtain, but for sustained use, a steel or bronze backed lead-tin bearing is preferred. The bore in the housings will require amendment to suit whichever is the chosen type. Refer to the housings for the fitting of the bearings. Ensure the oil holes are aligned before installing.

The inlet manifold assembly, *item 7*, is fabricated from copper tube and a brass or mild steel plate, brazed together. The plate is formed over a mandrel, 84 mm. in diameter, and holes drilled as shown. The connecting pipe is bent up from copper tube; both parts may require annealing to aid forming. Braze the two parts together, using a suitable flux and brazing rod. In the absence of brazing equipment, soft solder may be substituted: a fairly large iron will be needed. Finally, clean up, using emery or an acid dip.

FIG. 16 COMPLETED MODEL DISC TURBINE ENGINE MAIN COMPONENTS

The rotor assembly comprises of the discs, shaft, nut, rivet and a drive key. Assemble the discs to the shaft, using a plain nut to retain, and ensure that the rivet holes are in line, and the rivets enter satisfactorily.

Check the overall dimension of the stack, and compare to the relevant dimensions on the stator. Check the clearances between the end cover faces, and the shaft on the bearing bushes. A running clearance is required between the shaft and end of the bushes, with the rotor centralised in the stator. Use a shim between the end covers and stator, to obtain a clearance.

Mount the assembly between centres, and at a slow speed rotate the assembly. With a sharp tool, and a very low feed, trim the discs to size, to give a clearance in the bore of between 0.250 and 0.350 mm. on radius. Remove burr, and check for run-out. If more than 0.05 mm, adjust the side clearance to accommodate. A large slide clearance will not be detrimental to running, but will affect the output performance. Close the rivets, making sure they are flush to under flush. Remove the nut, and replace with a stiffnut. Check for static balance, drilling countersunk holes partially into the end discs until satisfactory. Balance is important as the turbine rotates at high speed. Assemble into the stator and end covers, tightening the fastenings as specified, and build on the intake manifold. Lubricate the bearings copiously, and rotate by hand, checking carefully for any tight spots or apparent foul points.

Place between centres, and with the housing supported by the cross-slide, and at a slow speed, rotate the turbine, gradually increasing speed up to about 1000 R.P.M. Watch for any tightness or increase in temperature. Run for 5 minutes, ensuring the bearings are kept well lubricated. Finally, when satisfied, remove from the lathe.

TESTING

When satisfied that the unit is turning freely, with no tightness or temperature rise, the unit can be tested using compressed air. This should be done initially, regardless of the medium to be used eventually. Using a flexible hose, connect to an air source, attaching the hose to the turbine with a hose clip. Between the turbine and the air supply, close to the turbine, provide an on/off valve, preferably of the ball type; for temporary use only, the hose may be squeezed in a vice, or by clamps. Place a guard over the turbine, and ensure that the exhaust ports are clear of obstruction. Check the air pressure, which must not exceed 2 bar, and slowly open the valve. The turbine will begin to rotate, and as the flow is increased, the speed will build up.

Run for no more than two minutes, stop, check the housing temperature. If cool to slightly warm, re-open the valve and continue running. At around 1.75 bar and 1.5 cfm, the turbine will attain a shaft speed of 20,000 R.P.M. At all times ensure a supply of oil to the bearings, and continually monitor the housing temperature. It should be noted that the prototype attained a speed of approximately 50,000 R.P.M. under no-load conditions; hence it is advised that a brake or dynometer be provided on the shaft.

Upon conclusion of a satisfactory operation on air, an alternative medium can be used to operate the turbine, such as steam from a model boiler. This model is not suitable for use with hot gas, such as is obtained by burning fuel in a suitable combustor.

At all times, ensure a suitable guard is in place, and observe sensible precautions when operating in the presence of other people.

This is a unique machine, and will provide plenty of scope for experimentation and development by the maker.

IMPORTANT!

The drawings which follow have been reduced from full size orginals. They have been reproduced in this book as large as possible to aid clarity and are thus not to a constant scale.

Measuring off drawings is bad practice anyway, but in this case attempts to do so will lead to disaster - you have been warned!

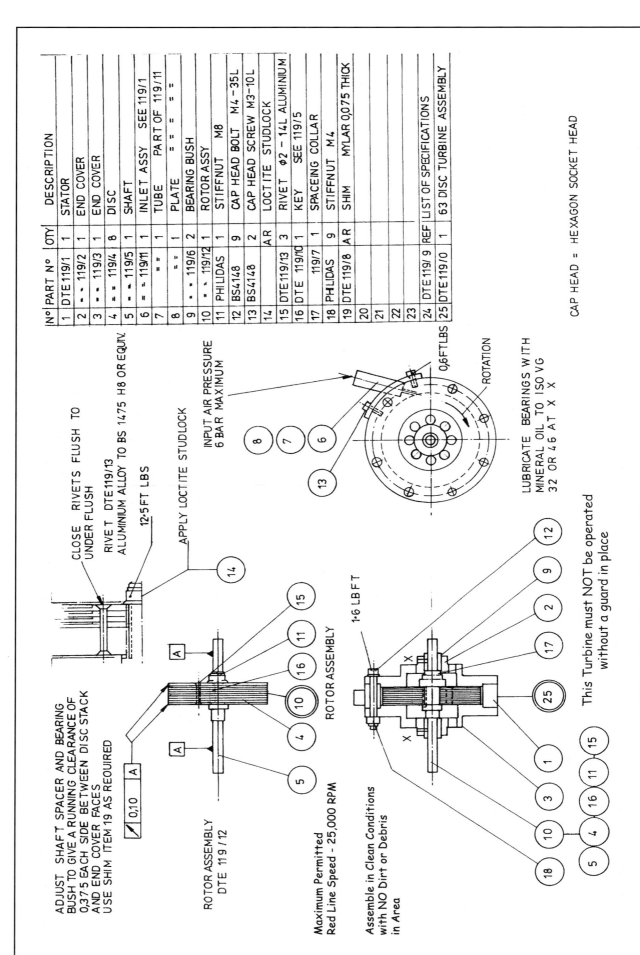

N°	PART N°	QTY	DESCRIPTION
1	DTE 119/1	1	STATOR
2	" " 119/2	1	END COVER
3	" " 119/3	1	END COVER
4	" " 119/4	8	DISC
5	" " 119/5	1	SHAFT
6	" " 119/11	1	INLET ASSY SEE 119/1
7	" " "	1	TUBE PART OF 119/11
8	" " "	1	PLATE " " "
9	" " 119/6	2	BEARING BUSH
10	" " 119/12	1	ROTOR ASSY
11	PHILIDAS	1	STIFFNUT M8
12	BS4148	9	CAP HEAD BOLT M4 -35L
13	BS4148	2	CAP HEAD SCREW M3-10L
14		AR	LOCTITE STUDLOCK
15	DTE119/13	3	RIVET ⌀2 - 14L ALUMINIUM
16	DTE 119/10	1	KEY SEE 119/5
17	119/7	1	SPACEING COLLAR
18	PHILIDAS	9	STIFFNUT M4
19	DTE 119/8	AR	SHIM MYLAR 0,075 THICK
20			
21			
22			
23			
24	DTE 119/ 9	REF	LIST OF SPECIFICATIONS
25	DTE119/0	1	63 DISC TURBINE ASSEMBLY

CAP HEAD = HEXAGON SOCKET HEAD

ADJUST SHAFT SPACER AND BEARING
BUSH TO GIVE A RUNNING CLEARANCE OF
0,375 EACH SIDE BETWEEN DISC STACK
AND END COVER FACES
USE SHIM ITEM 19 AS REQUIRED

CLOSE RIVETS FLUSH TO
UNDER FLUSH

RIVET DTE119/13
ALUMINIUM ALLOY TO BS 1475 H8 OR EQUIV.

12·5 FT LBS

APPLY LOCTITE STUDLOCK

INPUT AIR PRESSURE
6 BAR MAXIMUM

ROTOR ASSEMBLY
DTE 119 / 12

Maximum Permitted
Red Line Speed - 25,000 RPM

Assemble in Clean Conditions
with NO Dirt or Debris
in Area

ROTOR ASSEMBLY

0,6 FT LBS

ROTATION

LUBRICATE BEARINGS WITH
MINERAL OIL TO ISO VG
32 OR 46 AT X X

1·6 LB FT

This Turbine must NOT be operated
without a guard in place

MODEL DISC TURBINE ENGINE - GENERAL ARRANGEMENT AND LAYOUT

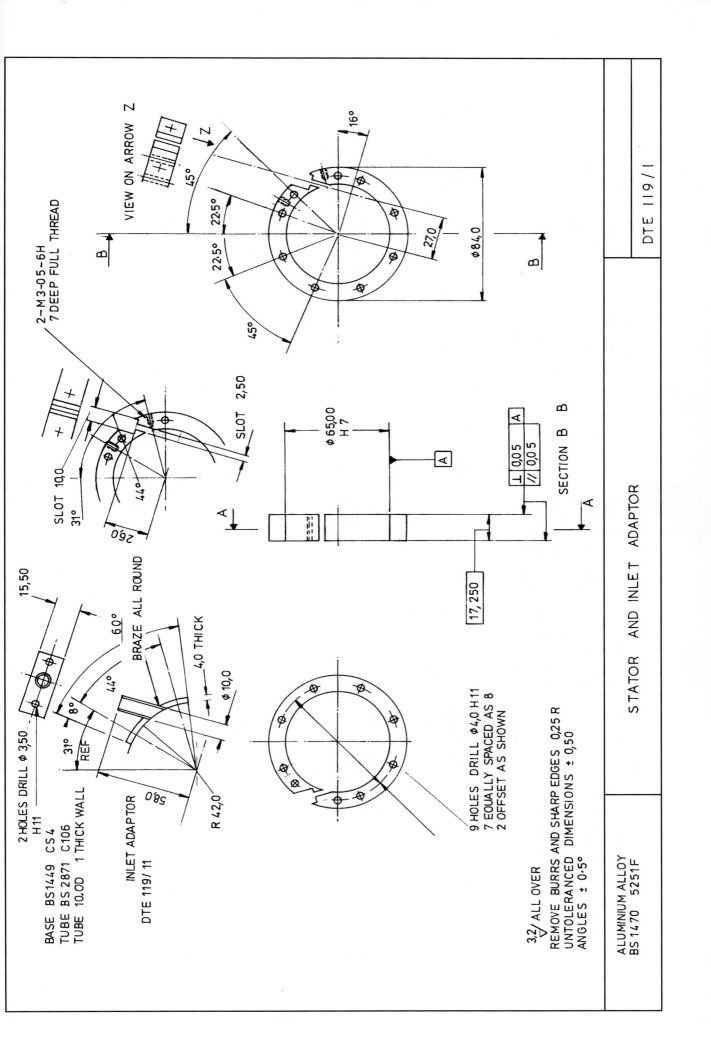

VIEW ON ARROW Z

2-M 3-05-6H
7 DEEP FULL THREAD

16°

45°

22·5°

22·5°

27,0

45°

Ø 84,0

B

B

SLOT 2,50

SLOT 10,0

31°

44°

26,0

Ø 65,00
H 7

A

A

A

⊥ | 0,05 | A
// | 0,05

SECTION B B

17,250

15,50

2 HOLES DRILL Ø 3,50
H11

BASE BS 1449 CS 4
TUBE BS 2871 C106
TUBE 10,0D 1 THICK WALL

60°

BRAZE ALL ROUND

8°

44°

4,0 THICK

Ø 10,0

31°

REF

58,0

R 42,0

INLET ADAPTOR
DTE 119/ 11

9 HOLES DRILL Ø 4,0 H11
7 EQUALLY SPACED AS 8
2 OFFSET AS SHOWN

3,2/ ALL OVER

REMOVE BURRS AND SHARP EDGES 0,25 R
UNTOLERANCED DIMENSIONS ± 0,50
ANGLES ± 0·5°

ALUMINIUM ALLOY
BS 1470 5251F

STATOR AND INLET ADAPTOR

DTE 119 / 1

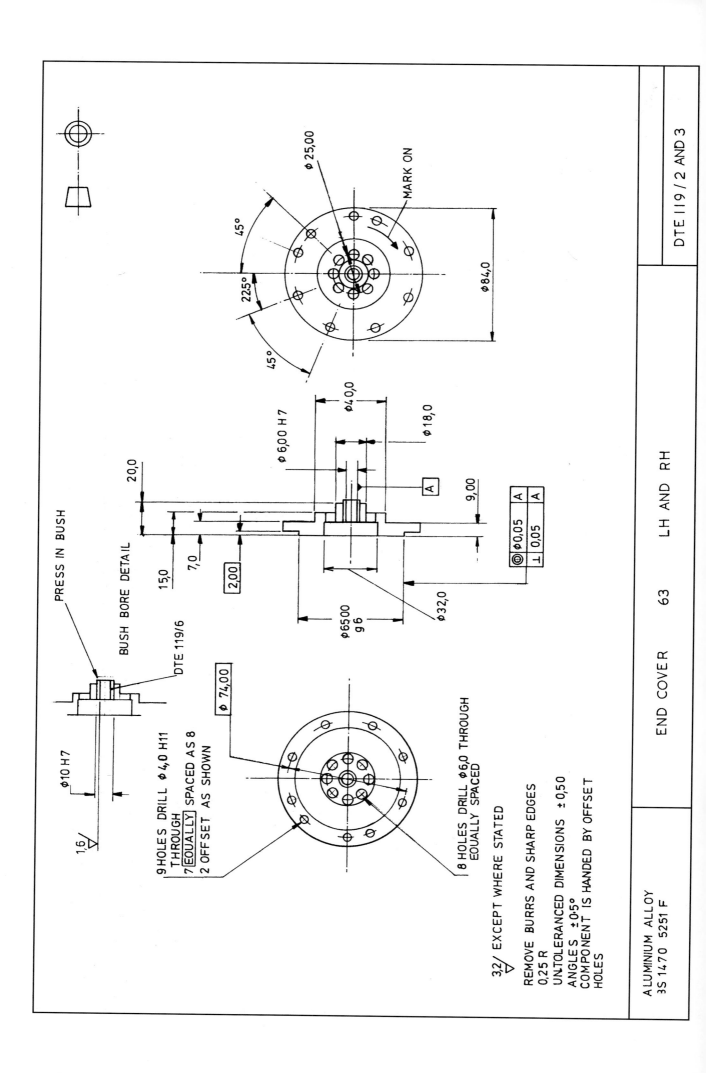

Φ 25,00

MARK ON

45°

225°

45°

Φ 84,0

Φ 40,0

Φ 6,00 H7

Φ 18,0

20,0

9,00

15,0

7,0

2,00

◎	Φ0,05	A
⊥	0,05	A

Φ6500
g6

Φ 32,0

PRESS IN BUSH

BUSH BORE DETAIL

DTE 119/6

Φ10 H7

1,6

9 HOLES DRILL Φ4,0 H11 THROUGH
7 EQUALLY SPACED AS 8
2 OFFSET AS SHOWN

Φ 74,00

8 HOLES DRILL Φ6,0 THROUGH
EQUALLY SPACED

3,2/ EXCEPT WHERE STATED
▽

REMOVE BURRS AND SHARP EDGES
0,25 R
UNTOLERANCED DIMENSIONS ±0,50
ANGLES ±0·5°
COMPONENT IS HANDED BY OFFSET
HOLES

ALUMINIUM ALLOY
3S 1470 5251 F

END COVER   63   LH AND RH

DTE 119 / 2 AND 3

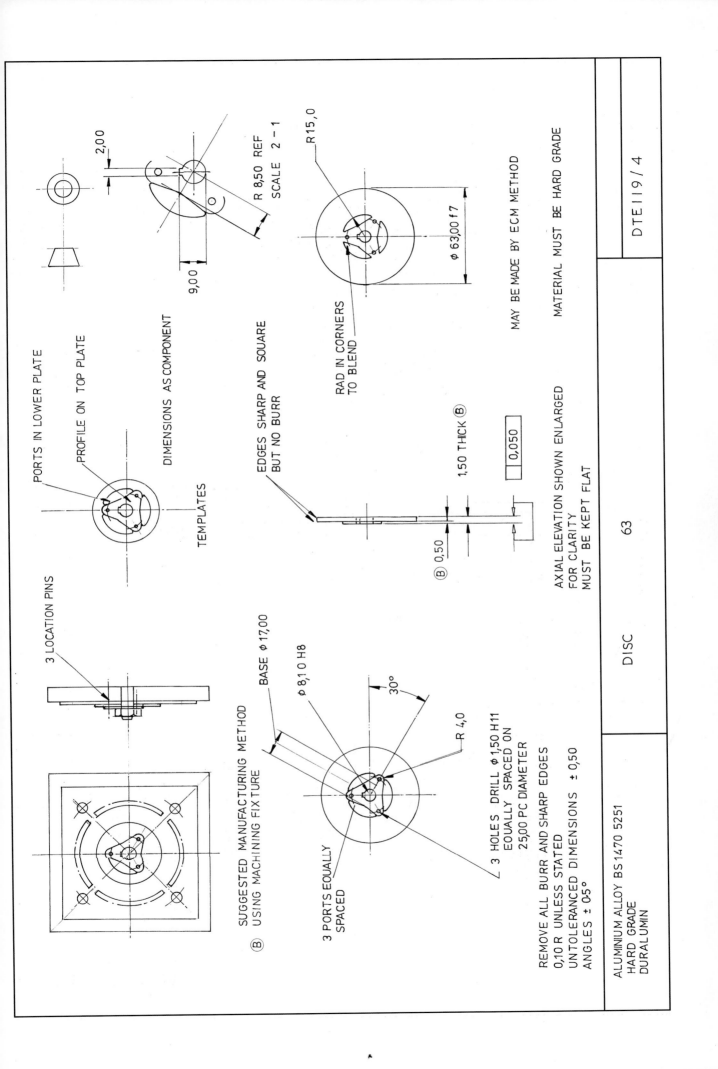

2,00

R 8,50 REF
SCALE 2 – 1

R15,0

Ø 63,00 f7

RAD IN CORNERS
TO BLEND

9,00

PORTS IN LOWER PLATE

PROFILE ON TOP PLATE

DIMENSIONS AS COMPONENT

TEMPLATES

EDGES SHARP AND SQUARE
BUT NO BURR

1,50 THICK (B)

0,050

(B) 0,50

AXIAL ELEVATION SHOWN ENLARGED
FOR CLARITY
MUST BE KEPT FLAT

MAY BE MADE BY ECM METHOD   MATERIAL MUST BE HARD GRADE

3 LOCATION PINS

(B) SUGGESTED MANUFACTURING METHOD
     USING MACHINING FIXTURE

BASE Ø 17,00

Ø 8,10 H8

R 4,0

30°

3 PORTS EQUALLY
SPACED

3 HOLES DRILL Ø 1,50 H11
EQUALLY SPACED ON
25,00 PC DIAMETER

REMOVE ALL BURR AND SHARP EDGES
0,10 R UNLESS STATED
UNTOLERANCED DIMENSIONS ± 0,50
ANGLES ± 0·5°

ALUMINIUM ALLOY BS 1470 5251
HARD GRADE
DURALUMIN

DISC

63

DTE119 / 4

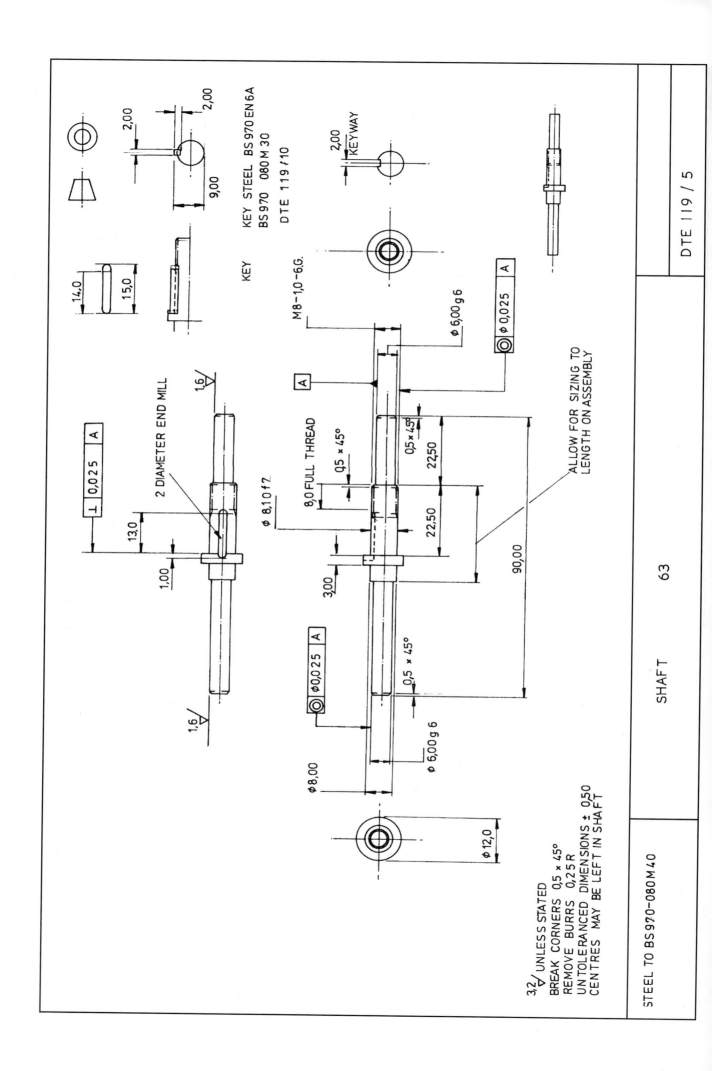

2,00

9,00

14,0

15,0

KEY STEEL BS 970 EN 6A
BS 970   080 M 30
DTE 119/10

KEY

M8-1,0-6.G.

⌀6,00 g6

| ◎ | ⌀ 0,025 | A |

A

63

SHAFT

DTE 119 / 5

2 DIAMETER END MILL

1,6

| ⊥ | 0,025 | A |

13,0

1,00

1,6

⌀ 8,10 f7

8,0 FULL THREAD

0,5 × 45°

0,5 × 45°

22,50

22,50

90,00

3,00

| ◎ | ⌀0,025 | A |

0,5 × 45°

⌀ 5,00 g 6

⌀8,00

⌀ 5,00 g 6

⌀12,0

2,00
KEYWAY

ALLOW FOR SIZING TO
LENGTH ON ASSEMBLY

3,2/ UNLESS STATED
BREAK CORNERS 0,5 × 45°
REMOVE BURRS 0,25 R
UNTOLERANCED DIMENSIONS ± 0,50
CENTRES MAY BE LEFT IN SHAFT

STEEL TO BS 970-080 M 40

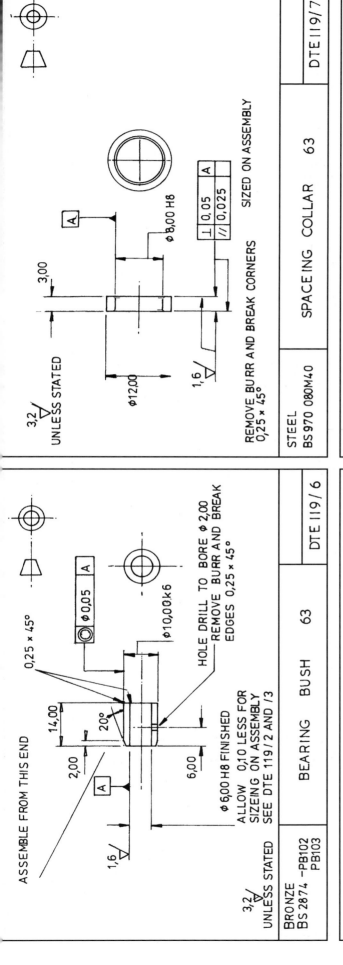

Top-left: SPACING COLLAR

3,2 / UNLESS STATED

3,00

Ø8,00 H8

Ø12,00

A

⊥	0,05	A
//	0,025	

1,6

REMOVE BURR AND BREAK CORNERS
0,25 × 45°   SIZED ON ASSEMBLY

STEEL
BS 970 080M40

SPACING COLLAR   63

DTE 119/7

Top-right: SPECIFICATIONS

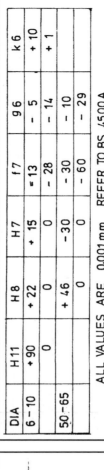

DIA	H11	H8	H7	f7	g6	k6
6 – 10	+ 90	+ 22	+ 15	– 13	– 5	+ 10
	0	0	0	– 28	– 14	+ 1
50 – 65		+ 46	– 30	– 30	– 10	– 10
		0	0	– 60	– 29	– 29

ALL VALUES ARE 0,001mm   REFER TO BS 4500A

TAP DRILL SIZE FOR M3 – DRILL. Ø 2,50
SOCKET HEAD SCREWS AND BOLTS TO BS 4148 GRADE 8,8 OR BETTER
TORQUE TIGHTENING VALUES ARE NOMINAL FOR OILED THREAD AND
MAY VARY BY 30%
DRILLED HOLE POSITIONS WITHIN ⊕ 0,10 OF TRUE POSITION
DRAWINGS AND GEOMETRIC TOLERANCES SEE BS 308–1984
STIFFNUTS ARE PHILIDAS OR AERO SPLIT NUTS
USE NUTS TO BS 3692–12 OR –8 AND APPLY LOCTITE IF NOT AVAILABLE
RIVETS ITEM 119/13 CUT FROM ALLOY BAR OR STANDARD CSK ITEM

SPECIFICATIONS   63

DTE 119/9

Bottom-left: BEARING BUSH

ASSEMBLE FROM THIS END

0,25 × 45°

Ø 0,05   A

Ø10,00 k6

14,00

2,00

20°

6,00

A

1,6

3,2 / UNLESS STATED

HOLE DRILL TO BORE Ø 2,00
REMOVE BURR AND BREAK
EDGES 0,25 × 45°

Ø 6,00 H8 FINISHED

ALLOW 0,10 LESS FOR
SIZEING ON ASSEMBLY
SEE DTE 119/2 AND /3

BRONZE
BS 2874 –PB102
PB103

BEARING   BUSH   63

DTE 119/6

Bottom-right: GASKET

Ø 74,00

Ø 65,00

Ø 84,0

45°

22,5°

9 HOLES Ø 4,0 H11
7 EQUALLY SPACED AS 8
2 OFFSET AS SHOWN

THICKNESS 0,075

MYLAR

GASKET   63

DTE 119/8

NOTES: